Well, at least there's some food, I'm starving.

This will do for supper.

Time to get some rest.

4

The next morning...

I will rest here for a bit.

14

CRACK

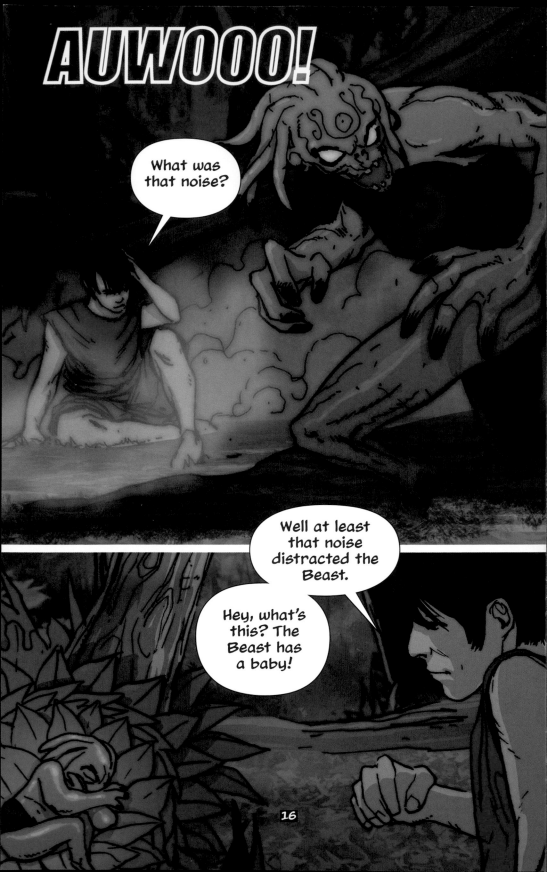

Chime,
give the Beast
her baby.

19

The Beast has
left the forest
– it will not
return.

Chime, you have saved the village. The villagers can now return.

I couldn't have done it without you.

Let's get back to the village.

FOR TEACHERS

About

SLIP STREAM

Slipstream is a series of expertly levelled books designed for pupils who are struggling with reading. Its unique three-strand approach through fiction, graphic fiction and non-fiction gives pupils a rich reading experience that will accelerate their progress and close the reading gap.

At the heart of every Slipstream graphic fiction book is a great story. Easily accessible words and phrases ensure that pupils both decode and comprehend, and the high interest stories really engage older struggling readers.

Whether you're using Slipstream Level 2 for Guided Reading or as an independent read, here are some suggestions:

1. Make each reading session successful. Talk about the text or pictures before the pupil starts reading. Introduce any unfamiliar vocabulary.

2. Encourage the pupil to talk about the book using a range of open questions. For example, how would they help people if they were a martial arts champion?

3. Discuss the differences between reading fiction, graphic fiction and non-fiction. What do they prefer?

Slipstream Level 2 photocopiable **WORKBOOK** ISBN: 978 1 4451 1797 3 available – download free sample worksheets from: www.franklinwatts.co.uk

For guidance, SLIPSTREAM Level 2 – Terror Beast has been approximately measured to:

National Curriculum Level: 2b
Reading Age: 7.6–8.0
Book Band: Purple

ATOS: 2.0*
Guided Reading Level: I
Lexile® Measure (confirmed): 190L

*Please check actual Accelerated Reader™ book level and quiz availability at www.arbookfind.co.uk